PHONICS
ACTIVITY
BOOK

Grade 2

Mc Graw Hill **Macmillan McGraw-Hill**

New York • Farmington

Macmillan/McGraw-Hill

A Division of The **McGraw·Hill** _Companies_

Macmillan/MacGraw-Hill
Two Penn Plaza
New York, New York 10121

Printed in the United States of America

ISBN 0-02-181278-0 / 2

Contents

Look at the pictures.
Read the words.
Then write the two words that tell about the picture.

1.   fright   bright   tight   light

_____   _____

2.   night   might   shy   sky

_____   _____

3.   sight   try   fly   by

_____ to _____

Long Vowels and Phonograms: /ī/-*ight*, -*y*   **I**

The letters **ight** and **y** stand for the phonograms you hear in these underlined words.

   The noise made <u>by</u> the truck gave <u>my</u> cat a <u>fright</u>.

Now finish each sentence below. Circle the word that completes the sentence. Then write the answer.

1. Do you and your brother often _____?

    right   light   fight

2. These old shoes are much too _____.

    sight   tight   might

3. I hope I get all the answers _____.

    knight   fright   right

4. That sad story made me _____.

    cry   fry   dry

5. I'll wash the dishes if you will _____ them.

    dry   by   fly

Say each picture name.
Read the words.
Write the word that belongs with each picture.

1.

tree
glee
see _____

2.

team
steam
dream _____

3.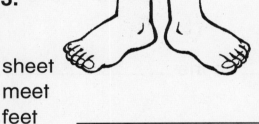

sheet
meet
feet _____

4.

see
beet
bee _____

5.

gleam
stream
steam _____

6.

sweet
beam
beet _____

7.

free
bee
street _____

8.

three
tree
street _____

Look at the pictures.
Read the words.
Then write the two words that tell about the picture.

1.

sheet   meet   street   cream

_____ on the _____

2.

three   tree   beam   beet

_____ on the _____

3.

beet   sweet   feet   dream

_____   _____

4.

bee   see   team   tree

_____ on a _____

Say each picture name. Read the words.
Write the word that belongs with each picture.

1.

dime
time _____

2.

kite
bike _____

3.

quite
bite _____

4.

crime
lime _____

5.

hike
bike _____

6.

kite
like _____

The letters **ike**, **ite** and **ime** stand for the phonograms you hear in these underlined words.

Would you <u>like</u> to <u>bite</u> a <u>lime</u>?

Now finish each sentence below. Circle the word that completes the sentence. Then write the answer.

1. My kitten's fur is _____.

   like   white   bite

2. Please come to school on _____.

   time   dime   kite

3. What kind of soup do you _____?

   quite   hike   like

4. I couldn't eat another _____.

   white   crime   bite

5. My hair isn't _____ as long as yours.

   quite   time   hike

6. This toy costs only a _____.

   kite   dime   time

Say each picture name.
Circle the letters that stand for the phonogram.
Then write the letters on the line to complete the word.

1.

ait ay

b_____

2.

ait ay

tr_____

3.

ait ay

cl_____

4.

ay ait

w_____

5.

ait ay

pl_____

6.

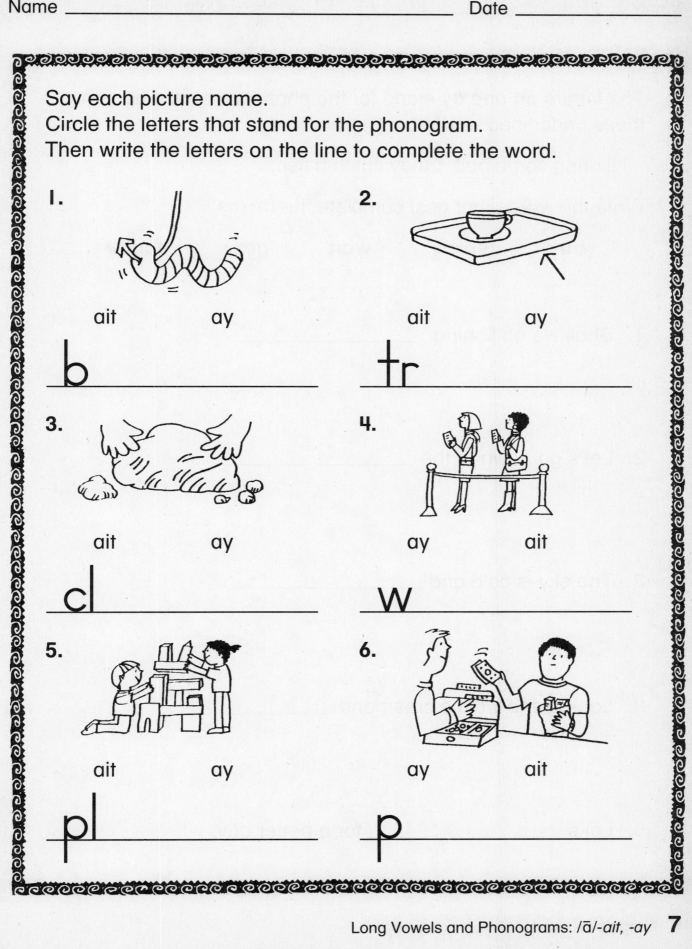

ay ait

p_____

The letters **ait** and **ay** stand for the phonograms you hear in these underlined words.

I'll bring some <u>bait</u>. I <u>may</u> catch a fish.

Write the words that best complete the rhyme.

bay   **spray**   **wait**   **gray**   **today**

1. Shall we go fishing _____?

2. Let's go down to the _____.

3. The sky is cold and _____.

4. Look at the waves crash and _____!

5. Let's _____ for a better day.

Name _____ Date _____

Say each picture name.
Circle the word that names the picture.

1. dry   fry

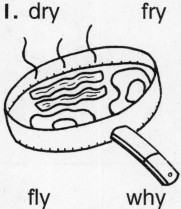

fly   why

2. hay   say

hike   like

3. bike   bright

meet   beet

4. cry   tight

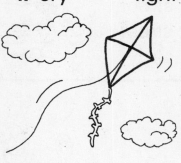

kite   bite

5. steam   team

tree   time

6. hike   spike

hay   stay

7. by   beam

bay   bee

8. right   kite

night   feet

9. time   dime

dry   try

Name _____ Date _____

Say each picture name.
Circle the word that names the picture.

1.
knight
kite
knee

2.
light
might
quite

3.
flee
fly
flight

4.
clay
cry
cream

5.
lime
light
like

6.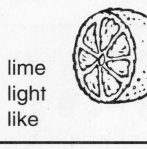
stream
street
stray

7.
fright
free
feet

8.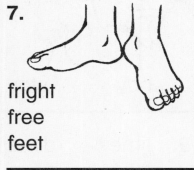
bait
bike
bite

9.
wait
bait
bay

10.
play
gray
pay

11.
try
tray
tree

12.
tray
bay
pay

Long Vowels and Phonograms Review: /ī/, /ā/, /ē/

Look at the pictures.
Read the words.
Then write the two words that tell about the picture.

1.   Park   Mark   far   car

_____ the _____ .

2.   tar   star   dark   park

_____ in the _____

3.   Bark   Park   shark   spark

_____ at a _____ .

Say each picture name.
Circle the letters that stand for the phonogram.
Then write the letters on the line to complete the word.

1.

   ar   ark

   p _____

2.

   ar   ark

   st _____

3.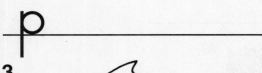

   ar   ark

   sh _____

4.

   ar   ark

   b _____

5.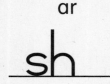

   ar   ark

   c _____

6.

   ar   ark

   t _____

Say each picture name.
Read the words.
Then write the word that belongs with each picture.

1.

those
home
hose
_____

2.

pose
hose
chose
_____

3.
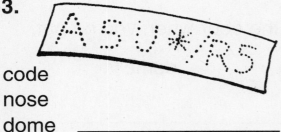
code
nose
dome
_____

4.

dome
those
close
_____

5.
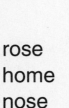
rose
home
nose
_____

6.

rose
rode
pose
_____

7.
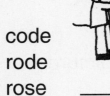
code
rode
rose
_____

8.
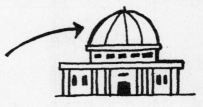
chose
code
dome
_____

MACMILLAN/McGRAW-HILL

The letters **ode**, **ose** and **ome** stand for the phonograms you hear in these underlined words.

Those two boys rode their bikes home.

Now finish each sentence below. Circle the word that completes the sentence. Then write the answer.

1. Let's use a secret _____ when we write.

 nose code dome

2. Please _____ the door when you go out.

 close chose dome

3. The city hall has a gold _____.

 nose dome rode

4. An elephant's _____ is called a trunk.

 nose code home

5. I'll be _____ before six o'clock.

 chose hose home

6. My dad asked us to _____ for a picture.

 code pose rose

Say each picture name. Read the words.
Write the word that belongs with each picture.

1.

cheer
clear _____

2.

tears
hears _____

3.

near
hear _____

4.

beard
feared _____

5.

hear
year _____

6.

deer
gear _____

The letters **eer** and **ear** stand for the phonograms you hear in these underlined words.

We often see <u>deer</u> in the woods this time of <u>year</u>.

Now finish each sentence below. Circle the word that completes the sentence. Then write the answer.

1. There was a _____ of paint on his shirt.

   gear   smear   steer

2. The sun shone in a _____ sky.

   clear   tear   deer

3. I hope these flowers will _____ you up.

   cheer   clear   hear

4. That store is _____ my house.

   dear   fear   near

5. We saw two _____ in the field.

   year   deer   hear

6. Mom showed us how to _____ the wagon.

   deer   spear   steer

MACMILLAN/McGRAW-HILL

Look at the pictures.
Read the words.
Then write the two words that tell about the picture.

1.   caught   taught   mall   ball

_____   the   _____

2.   stall   small   fall   tall

_____   and   _____

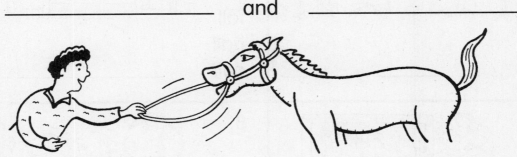

3.   brought   fought   stall   call

_____   into the   _____

Variant Vowels and Phonograms: /ô/-all, -aught, -ought   **17**

Name _____   Date _____

Say each picture name.
Read the words.
Then write the word that belongs with each picture.

1.

bought
fought
taught   _____

2.

caught
wall
call   _____

3.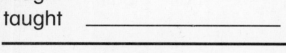

brought
ball
tall   _____

4.

thought
bought
fought   _____

5.

ball
stall
wall   _____

6.

fall
hall
call   _____

7.

taught
caught
bought   _____

8.

wall
fought
fall   _____

18 Variant Vowels and Phonograms: /ô/-all, -aught, -ought

Name _____ Date _____

Say each picture name.
Circle the letters that stand for the phonogram.
Then write the letters on the line to complete the word.

1.

ark   ar

b _____

2.

ose   ome

h _____

3.

ark   eer

d _____

4.

aught   ar

c _____

5.

ear   ar

h _____

6.

ose   ome

d _____

7.

ode   ose

r _____

8.

ear   all

w _____

9.

ought   ose

th _____

Name _____ Date _____

Say each picture name.
Circle the word that names the picture.

1.

taught
tall
call

2.

mark
mall
park

3.
call
code
caught

4.

beard
bird
star

5.
hall
home
hark

6.

nose
those
hose

7.

star
sheer
shark

8.

ball
bought
fought

9.

cheer
chose
clear

10.
call
close
code

11.
rode
rose
fear

12.
stall
steer
star

Say each picture name. Read the words.
Write the word that belongs with each picture.

1.

fools
tools _____

2.

pool
spool _____

3.

moon
noon _____

4.

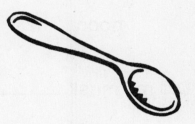

soon
spoon _____

5.

cool
school _____

6.

spool
school _____

The letters **ool** and **oon** stand for the phonograms you hear in these underlined words.

   School will start soon.

Now finish each sentence below. Circle the word that completes the sentence. Then write the answer.

1. We eat lunch at _____.

   noon   moon   spoon

2. I'll eat my soup with a _____.

   noon   moon   spoon

3. Did my mask _____ you?

   school   tool   fool

4. I need to buy a _____ of thread.

   cool   spool   fool

5. The night air was _____.

   cool   pool   tool

6. The _____ was shining in the sky.

   spoon   moon   soon

Name _____   Date _____

Say each picture name.
Read the words.
Then write the word that belongs with each picture.

1.

care
hare
chair   _____

2.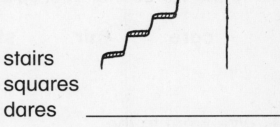

stairs
squares
dares   _____

3.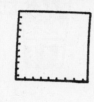

scare
square
stare   _____

4.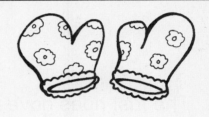

fair
hair
pair   _____

5.

care
share
chair   _____

6.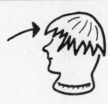

fair
hair
pair   _____

7.

scare
spare
stair   _____

8.

stare
share
scare   _____

Variant Vowels and Phonograms: /âr/-air, -are **23**

The letters **are** and **air** stand for the phonograms you hear in these underlined words.

Do you <u>dare</u> to go on rides at the <u>fair</u>?

Write the words that best complete the rhyme.

care   **fair**   **stare**   **hair**   **scare**

1. We went to the _____.

2. The fast rides gave us a _____.

3. We saw a man with pink _____.

4. We couldn't help but _____.

5. The man just grinned. He didn't _____.

Look at the pictures. Read the words.
Then write the two words that tell about the picture.

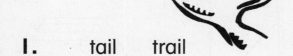

1.   tail   trail   quail   whale

_____ of a _____

2.   jail   pail   sale   stale

_____ for _____

3.   mail   snail   scale   bale

_____ on a _____

4.   nail   pale   rail   fail

_____ in a _____

Say each picture name.
Circle the word that names the picture.

1.

fail
mail
nail

2.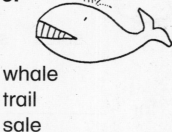

sail
snail
stale

3.

sale
scale
tale

4.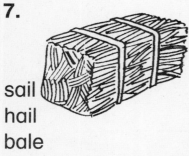

moon
male
tale

5.

whale
trail
sale

6.

bale
pail
wail

7.

sail
hail
bale

8.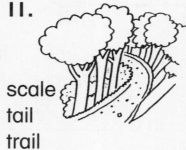

tail
fail
snail

9.

tale
sale
pale

10.

snail
nail
quail

11.

scale
tail
trail

12.

pail
rail
nail

Say each picture name.
Circle the letters that stand for the phonogram.
Then write the letters on the line to complete the word.

1.

eel   eed

f _____

2.

eel   eed

s _____

3.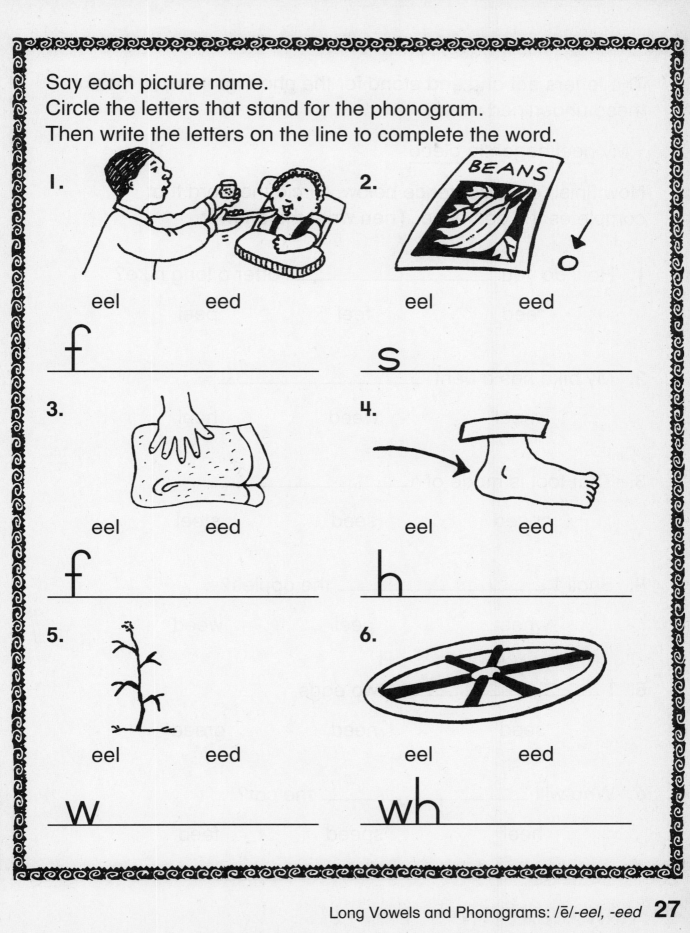

eel   eed

f _____

4.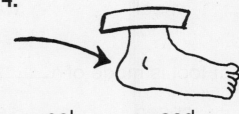

eel   eed

h _____

5.

eel   eed

w _____

6.

eel   eed

wh _____

The letters **eel** and **eed** stand for the phonograms you hear in these underlined words.

My <u>heel</u> began to <u>bleed</u>.

Now finish each sentence below. Circle the word that completes the sentence. Then write the answer.

1. How do you _____ after a long hike?

    feed   feel   peel

2. My bike has a bent _____.

    wheel   weed   heel

3. That tool is made of _____.

    speed   seed   steel

4. Shall I _____ the apples?

    wheel   peel   weed

5. I _____ two eggs.

    seed   need   greed

6. Who will _____ the cat?

    heel   speed   feed

Say each picture name.
Circle the word that names the picture.

1.

noon
soon
moon

2.

pail
hail
wail

3.

hair
share
chair

4.

steel
wheel
heel

5.

peel
kneel
wheel

6.

spoon
noon
soon

7.

mail
fail
sail

8.

need
feed
weed

9.

scale
whale
tale

10.

stare
spare
square

11.

speed
weed
bleed

12.

pool
spool
fool

MACMILLAN/McGRAW-HILL

Name _____   Date _____

Say each picture name.
Circle the letters that stand for the phonogram.
Then write the letters on the line to complete the word.

1.

ail   are

sn_____

2.

ool   oon

sp_____

3.

eed   are

sp_____

4.

ail   are

h_____

5.

ool   ail

t_____

6.

air   ail

f_____

7.

eel   ool

p_____

8.

eel   ale

wh_____

9.

are   ale

sc_____

MACMILLAN/McGRAW-HILL

Look at the pictures.
Read the words.
Then write the two words that tell about the picture.

1. books   brook   woods   hood

_____ in the _____

2. Look   Cook   book   hook

_____ at a _____.

3. good   wood   crook   cook

_____   _____

The letters **ook** and **ood** stand for the phonograms you hear in these underlined words.

   We <u>stood</u> on the hill and <u>took</u> a <u>look</u>.

Now finish each sentence below. Circle the word that completes the sentence. Then write the answer.

1. Her coat has a _____.

   good   wood   hood

2. Hang your hat on a _____.

   hook   cook   took

3. We need some _____ for the fire.

   look   wood   good

4. Who _____ my mittens?

   took   look   stood

5. Would you like to read a _____?

   shook   brook   book

6. This story is really _____.

   hood   good   stood

MACMILLAN/McGRAW-HILL

Name _____   Date _____

Look at the pictures.
Read the words.
Then write the two words that tell about the picture.

1.   Sue   Blue      grew   crew

_____   _____.

2.   drew   new      chew   clue

_____   _____.

3.   Chew   Flew      dew   stew

_____   the   _____.

The letters **ew** and **ue** stand for the phonograms you hear in these underlined words.

What's <u>new</u>? Here is a <u>clue</u>. It is <u>blue</u>.

Write the words that best complete the rhyme.

true   **new**   **crew**   **grew**   **blue**

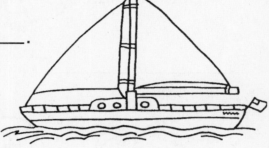

1. Our boat is _____.

2. It is painted _____.

3. We need some people for the _____.

4. The number of sailors _____.

5. This is really _____.

MACMILLAN/McGRAW-HILL

Say each picture name. Read the words.
Write the word that belongs with each picture.

1.

farm
harm _____

2.

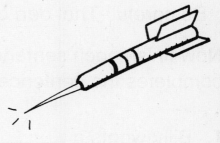

part
dart _____

3.

charm
cart _____

4.

arm
art _____

5.

start
smart _____

6.

cart
tart _____

Name _____ Date _____

The letters **art** and **arm** stand for the phonograms you hear in these underlined words.

Be careful! That <u>dart</u> could <u>harm</u> you.

Now finish each sentence below. Circle the word that completes the sentence. Then write the answer.

1. Billy wants a _____ in the play.

    part   tart   smart

2. My little dog is very _____.

    dart   cart   smart

3. We used clay in _____.

    start   art   cart

4. Kate's bracelet has a silver _____ on it.

    start   harm   charm

5. My dad grew up on a _____.

    farm   harm   charm

6. A little rain will do us no _____.

    farm   harm   arm

Look at the pictures.
Read the words.
Then write the two words that tell about the picture.

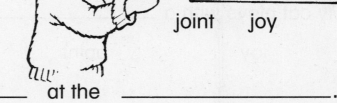

1. Toy   Point   joint   joy

_____ at the _____.

2. toy   point   joint   joy

_____ brings _____

3. boy   joy   Roy   toy

_____ named _____

Name _____   Date _____

The letters **oy** and **oint** stand for the phonograms you hear in these underlined words.

Point to the toy you want.

Now finish each sentence below. Circle the word that completes the sentence. Then write the answer.

1. My cat plays with a _____ mouse.

    joy   point   toy

2. My teacher's baby is a _____.

    point   boy   joint

3. I have a pain in my hip _____.

    toy   joy   joint

4. This pencil has a sharp _____.

    point   joint   boy

5. The new puppy gave us great _____.

    joy   point   Roy

6. My dad's name is _____.

    Joy   toy   Roy

38 Diphthongs and Phonograms: /oi/-*oy*, -*oint*

Name _____ Date _____

Say each picture name.
Circle the letters that stand for the phonogram.
Then write the letters on the line to complete the word.

1.

oy   ook

b _____

2.

ew   ook

cr _____

3.

oy   art

t _____

4.

arm   ood

h _____

5.

ue   art

c _____

6.

oint   ew

p _____

Name _____ Date _____

Say each picture name.
Circle the word that names the picture.

1. hood wood  stood good	**2.** crew stood  stew glue	**3.** flew harm  few farm
4. boy joint  toy blue	**5.** shook crook  book cook	**6.** brew blew  glue clue
7. joint pew  point took	**8.** smart dart  due drew	**9.** hook book  look brook

40 Variant Vowels/Diphthongs and Phonograms Review: /ü/, /u̇/, /är/, /oi/

Name _____ Date _____

Say each picture name.
Circle the letters that stand for the phonogram.
Then write the letters on the line to complete the word.

1.

oop   oot

sh___

2.

oop   oot

h___

3.

oop   oot

l___

4.

oop   oot

r___

5.

oop   oot

dr___

6.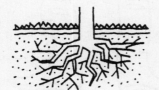

oop   oot

sc___

7.

oop   oot

tr___

8.

oop   oot

b___

9.

oop   oot

c___

Name _____   Date _____

Say each picture name. Read the words.
Write the word that belongs with each picture.

1.

swoop
hoop _____

2.

root
hoot _____

3.

stoop
troop _____

4.

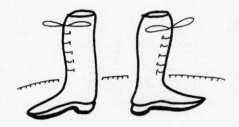

roots
boots _____

5.

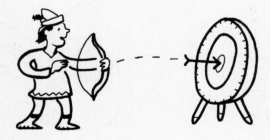

shoot
loot _____

6.

scoop
whoop _____

MACMILLAN/McGRAW-HILL

Name _____   Date _____

Look at the pictures.
Read the words.
Then write the two words that tell about the picture.

1.   draw   claw   talk   chalk

_____ with _____

2.   talk   stalk   law   claw

_____ about a _____

3.   straws   paws   talk   walk

_____ that _____

The letters **alk** and **aw** stand for the phonograms you hear in these underlined words.

I ate a <u>stalk</u> of <u>raw</u> celery.

Now finish each sentence below. Circle the word that completes the sentence. Then write the answer.

1. Will you _____ to school with me?

      talk   chalk   walk

2. Did you and Grandma _____?

      talk   chalk   walk

3. We write on the board with _____.

      stalk   chalk   talk

4. Mom cut the wood with a _____.

      saw   claw   jaw

5. I drink my milk through a _____.

      draw   straw   flaw

6. The kitten is licking its _____.

      law   saw   paw

Name _____ Date _____

Say each picture name. Read the words.
Write the word that belongs with each picture.

1.

chore
core _____

2.

for
sore _____

3.

store
snore _____

4.

snore
sore _____

5.

store
shore _____

6.
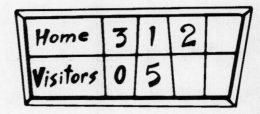

shore
score _____

The letters **or** and **ore** stand for the phonograms you hear in these underlined words.

The team <u>wore</u> blue shorts <u>for</u> the game.

Write the words that best complete the rhyme.

more   **for**   **score**   **tore**   **sore**

1. Two to five is the _____.

2. We need to get three _____!

3. What are you stopping _____?

4. "My leg is _____."

5. "And my shorts just _____!"

MACMILLAN/McGRAW-HILL

Name _____   Date _____

Say each picture name.
Read the words.
Then write the word that belongs with each picture.

1.

tow
throw
toast _____

2.
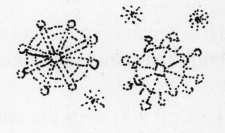
snow
slow
show _____

3.

mow
low
sow _____

4.

boast
bow
blow _____

5.
mow
throw
stow _____

6.

coast
toast
roast _____

7.

crow
sow
coast _____

8.

grow
row
low _____

Name _____ Date _____

The letters **oast** and **ow** stand for the phonograms you hear in these underlined words.

<u>Snow</u> fell along the <u>coast</u>.

Now finish each sentence below. Circle the word that completes the sentence. Then write the answer.

1. Can you hear the wind _____?

   mow   tow   blow

2. We went to see a puppet _____.

   show   snow   sow

3. For dinner we will _____ some meat.

   boast   roast   coast

4. Who ate the _____?

   toast   tow   boast

5. Her dress has a red _____.

   grow   show   bow

6. I don't like it when you _____ about your new clothes.

   coast   boast   toast

MACMILLAN/McGRAW-HILL

Name _____   Date _____

Say each picture name.
Circle the letters that stand for the phonogram.
Then write the letters on the line to complete the word.

1.

oot   ow

b _____

2.

oop   ore

sc _____

3.

alk   oast

t _____

4.

aw   oop

dr _____

5.

oast   ore

c _____

6.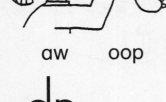

ow   ore

sh _____

7.

oast   oop

c _____

8.

oast   ore

t _____

9.

aw   ow

r _____

Name _____ Date _____

Say each picture name.
Circle the word that names the picture.

1. stoop hoot	2. for nor	3. saw straw
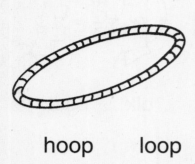	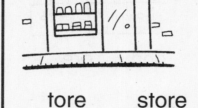	
hoop loop	tore store	sow slow
4. chalk chore	5. show shoot	6. tore tow

claw stalk	shore scoot	toast toot
7. score coop	8. snow snore	9. blow bow

scoot scoop	nor store	bore boot

Say each picture name. Read the words.
Write the word that belongs with each picture.

1.

house
blouse _____

2.

shout
scout _____

3.

sprout
trout _____

4.

mouse
house _____

5.

house
blouse _____

6.

snout
spout _____

The letters **out** and **ouse** stand for the phonograms you hear in these underlined words.

The <u>scout</u> meeting will be at my <u>house</u>.

Now finish each sentence below. Circle the word that completes the sentence. Then write the answer.

1. A teapot has a _____.

       pout   spout   scout

2. A tiny plant is a _____.

      sprout   shout   trout

3. A nest is a bird's _____.

      blouse   mouse   house

4. A kind of shirt is called a _____.

      blouse   mouse   house

5. At the ballgame we yell and _____.

      sprout   trout   shout

6. My sister has a pet _____.

      blouse   mouse   house

Say each picture name.
Circle the letters that stand for the phonogram.
Then write the letters on the line to complete the word.

1.

    eat   eak

b _____

2.

    eat   eak

p _____

3.

    eat   eak

b _____

4.

    eat   eak

sp _____

5.

    eat   eak

wh _____

6.

    eat   eak

tr _____

The letters **eat** and **eak** stand for the phonograms you hear in these underlined words.

Should we <u>sneak</u> into the kitchen for a <u>treat</u>?

Now finish each sentence below. Circle the word that completes the sentence. Then write the answer.

1. When you play a game, never _____.

   heat   meat   cheat

2. If you squeeze this toy, it will _____.

   seat   squeak   weak

3. The tiny kitten was very _____.

   wheat   weak   speak

4. Dan keeps his room clean and _____.

   neat   meat   beat

5. I'm cold! Please turn on the _____.

   beat   treat   heat

6. This hose has a _____.

   leak   peak   beak

Name _____   Date _____

Say each picture name.
Circle the word that names the picture.

1.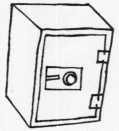

safe
state
shave

2.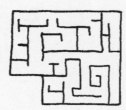

mate
gaze
maze

3.

pave
save
wave

4.

crave
cave
gave

5.

grate
graze
grave

6.

plate
slate
late

7.

wave
save
shave

8.

haze
hate
pave

9.

blaze
maze
graze

Name _____   Date _____

Say each picture name.
Circle the letters that stand for the phonogram.
Then write the letters on the line to complete the word.

1.

ave   ate

s _____

2.

ave   ate

w _____

3.

ave   aze

g _____

4.

ave   ate

sh _____

5.

afe   ate

s _____

6.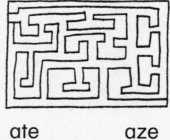

ate   aze

m _____

Name _____ Date _____

Look at the pictures. Read the words.
Then write the two words that tell about the picture.

1. gown   chow   hound   clown

_____ for the _____

2. crown   pound   cow   town

_____ on a _____

3. drown   frown   clown   crown

_____ on a _____

4. Sound   Pound   brown   down

_____ it _____.

Name _____   Date _____

The letters **ound**, **ow**, and **own** stand for the phonograms you hear in these underlined words.

The <u>hound</u> barked at the <u>brown</u> <u>cow</u>.

Now finish each sentence below. Circle the word that completes the sentence. Then write the answer.

1. The kite fell to the _____.

      ground   pound   wound

2. After you sing, take a _____.

      how   chow   bow

3. The queen wore a beautiful _____.

      town   gown   down

4. Look at what I _____!

      round   mound   found

5. My grandma lives in a small _____.

      town   down   clown

6. Come into the house right _____!

      how   now   cow

Name _____ Date _____

Say each picture name.
Circle the word that names the picture.

1.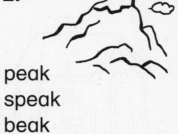
treat
wheat
heat

2.
peak
speak
beak

3.
mound
mouse
meat

4.
snout
squeak
scout

5.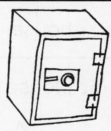
safe
state
speak

6.
bound
found
hound

7.
shave
store
wave

8.
down
gown
frown

9.
clown
chow
cow

10.
cave
creak
crate

11.
blaze
blouse
bleat

12.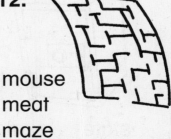
mouse
meat
maze

Say each picture name.
Circle the word that names the picture.

1. brown   clown

gown   chow

2. heat   how

house   hound

3. shave   save

shout   sound

4. shout   sneak

sound   snout

5. blouse   blaze

bleak   brave

6. blaze   blouse

beak   beat

7. safe   save
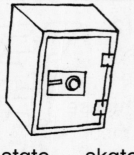
state   skate

8. heat   haze

wave   wheat

9. squeak   bleak

late   leak

The Complete *Love* Wedding Planner

Wedding Checklist

12 months before

- ☐ Finalize a wedding date
- ☐ Find and reserve the venue
- ☐ Choose your wedding party
- ☐ Set a date
- ☐ Reserve a block of hotel rooms for out-of-town guests
- ☐ Book a photographer for engagement photo
- ☐ Choose a wedding style
- ☐ Begin shopping for dresses

9 months before

- ☐ Confirm theme + color palette
- ☐ Have a wedding dress altered
- ☐ Choose + orders invitations
- ☐ Shop for hair accessories, jewelry, shoes
- ☐ Start planning your honeymoon
- ☐ Begin shopping for wedding party dresses + suits
- ☐ Research hair + makeup artists
- ☐ Research required insurance venue, wedding, event
- ☐ Set up a gift registry

6 months before

- ☐ Send out save the dates
- ☐ Meet with celebrant/officiant
- ☐ Decide on groom's groomsmen attire
- ☐ Choose a gift for wedding party
- ☐ Book a hotel if you plan to stay there for the night of the wedding
- ☐ Research and order cake
- ☐ Meet with the vendor to finalize all selections
- ☐ Choose wedding favors
- ☐ Finalize guest list

3 months before

- ☐ Send wedding invitation
- ☐ Obtain marriage license
- ☐ Begin to write vows
- ☐ Finalize full day timeline
- ☐ Finalize menu with caterer
- ☐ Send the draft run sheet to vendors
- ☐ Confirm ceremony running order with celebrant/officiant
- ☐ Order gift for the bridal party, parents + each other

Overview

WEDDING DATE .... BUDGET .... COLOUR SCHEME ....

STYLE: VINTAGE / ROMANTIC / CLASSIC / RETRO / MODERN / OTHER ....

WEDDING CEREMONY

CEREMONY LOCATION .... CEREMONY TIME .... TO ....

ADDRESS .... NUMBER OF GUESTS ....

WEDDING RECEPTION

RECEPTION LOCATION .... RECEPTION TIME .... TO ....

ADDRESS .... NUMBER OF GUESTS ....

BRIDESMAIDS

GROOMS

IMPORTANT DATES

ENGAGEMENT PARTY .... TO ....

BRIDAL SHOWER .... TO ....

BACHELOR PARTY .... TO ....

REHEARSAL DINNER .... TO ....

BRIDAL SHOWER .... TO ....

HONEYMOON .... TO ....

Wedding Attire Budget

Item	Budget	Spent	Paid
Engagement Party Outfit (plus shoes and accessories)			
Engagement Photos Outfit (plus shoes and accessories)			
Bridal Shower Outfit (plus shoes and accessories)			
Bachelor / Bachelorette Outfit (plus shoes and accessories)			
Rehearsal Dinner Outfit (plus shoes and accessories)			
Wedding Dress			
Wedding Dress Alterations			
Specialty Undergarments			
Veil, Wedding Shoes, and Bridal Jewelry / Accessories			
Groom's Tux + Shoes			
Reception Outfit (if you're changing out of your dress) or After Party Outfit			
Post-Wedding Brunch Outfit (plus shoes and accessories)			
Wedding Dress Cleaning and Preservation			

NOTES ....
....
....
....
....
....
....
....
....
....
....

Wedding Beauty Budget

Item	Budget	Spent	Paid
Pre-Wedding Haircuts or Color			
Waxing			
Facials			
Mani-Pedi			
Professional Shave			
Tips (normally around 20% for any pre-wedding beauty treatments)			
Spray Tan			
Lash Extensions			
Hair Trial Appointment			
Day-of Wedding Hairstyle			
Makeup Trial Appointment			
Day-of Wedding Makeup			

NOTES ....
....
....
....
....
....
....
....
....
....
....
....
....
....
....
....
....
....

Wedding Cake Budget

Item	Budget	Spent	Paid
Cake Display / Cake Cutting			
Sheet Cake for extra servings			
Specialty Design Elements (like sugar flowers or hand painting)			
Cake Topper			
Cake Stand			
Cake-Cutting Fee			
Delivery Fee			
Additional Desserts (if you're doing a dessert table/station)			
Preservation Kit for one-year anniversary			

NOTES ....
....
....
....
....
....
....
....
....
....
....
....
....
....
....
....
....
....
....

Wedding Ceremony Budget

Item	Budget	Spent	Paid
Ceremony Site (if separate from reception venue)			
Church Donation			
Officiant Fee			
Marriage License			
Ceremony Accessories (ring pillow, flower girl basket, unity candle, etc.)			

NOTES ....
....
....
....
....
....
....
....
....
....
....
....
....
....
....
....
....
....
....
....
....
....
....

Wedding Drinks Budget

Item	Budget	Spent	Paid
Cocktail Hour Drinks			
Reception Drinks			
Champagne Toast			
Open Bar / Hosted Beer & Wine / Specialty Cocktails			
Bartender Service			
Mixers			
Coffee / Tea			
Non-alcoholic Beverages			
Glassware (if not included in your catering package)			
Bar Signage			
Corkage Fees (if you opt to BYO)			
Liquor License (if not provided by venue or caterer)			
Bartender Gratuity			

NOTES ....
....
....
....
....
....
....
....
....
....
....
....
....
....
....
....

Wedding Flowers Budget

Item	Budget	Spent	Paid
Bouquets (for bride and brides-maids, and perhaps a toss bou-quet)			
Boutonnières (for groom, grooms-men, fathers and/or grandfathers)			
Corsages for Mothers / Grand-mothers			
Flowers and Accessories for the Flower Girl / Ring Bearer			
Ceremony Arch / Chuppah			
Ceremony Arrangements			
Reception Centerpieces (for guest tables, guest book table, food sta-tions, etc.)			
Wedding Cake Flowers (if addi-tional cake décor is needed)			
Wedding Chalkboards / Signage			
Specialty Décor Rentals (e.g. tent-ing, lanterns, candelabras, etc.)			
Delivery Fees			

NOTES ....
....
....
....
....
....
....
....
....
....
....
....
....
....
....

Wedding Food Budget

Item	Budget	Spent	Paid
Tasting Appointment (if not complimentary with your catering package)			
Rehearsal Dinner			
Passed Hors D'oeuvres			
Plated, Buffet, or Family-Style Meal			
Food Stations			
Service Staff			
Catering Equipment (such as plates, silverware, glassware, serving platters, etc.)			
Catering Rentals (such as tables, chairs, linens, etc.)			
Vendor Meals (it's nice to feed your photographer)			
Tax and Gratuity (sometimes called the "service charge")			
Setup and/or Cleanup Fees			
Bar/Beverage Service (see "Drinks" above; may be included in your catering package)			

NOTES ....
....
....
....
....
....
....
....
....
....
....

Wedding Invitations and Paper Budget

Item	Budget	Spent	Paid
Engagement Party Invitations			
Save The Dates			
Wedding Invitations (including inserts like RSVP cards or maps)			
Rehearsal Dinner Invitations			
Post Wedding Brunch Invitations			
Envelopes (note that specialty size envelopes will be more expensive to ship)			
Postage (for invitations and RSVP envelopes, as well as thank you cards)			
Return Address Labels			
Wedding Ceremony Programs			
Wedding Reception Paper Goods			
Escort Cards			
Place Cards			
Menu Cards			
Custom Napkins			
Favor Labels			
Thank You Cards			

NOTES ....
....
....
....
....
....
....
....
....
....

Wedding DJ and Gifts Budget

Item	Budget	Spent	Paid
Wedding Favors			
Wedding Party Gifts			
Gifts for your Flower Girl(s) or Ring Bearer(s)			
Spouse Gift			
Parents Gifts			
Welcome Baskets for out-of-town guests			
Ceremony Musicians			
Cocktail Hour Music			
Reception DJ or Live Band			
Microphone (for wedding ceremony and reception toasts)			
Sound-system or extra speakers			
Photo Booth & Dance Floor Lighting (if your DJ provides these extra services)			

NOTES ....
....
....
....
....
....
....
....
....
....
....
....
....
....

Wedding Photography and Videography Budget

Item	Budget	Spent	Paid
Engagement Session			
Rehearsal Dinner Coverage			
Wedding Day Coverage			
Albums or Prints			
Same Day Edit			
Raw Footage			
Highlight Reel			
Feature Film			

NOTES
....
....
....
....
....
....
....
....
....
....
....
....
....
....
....
....
....
....
....
....
....

Wedding Reception Budget

Item	Budget	Spent	Paid
Room Rental Fee			
Venue Deposit			
Ceremony Fee (if ceremony is being held at reception venue)			
Additional Rentals (such as tables, chairs, china, etc. if not provided by caterer)			
Dance Floor Rental (if not already installed/included)			
Parking Fees			
Liability Insurance			
Tax and Service Fees			
Security (some venues require it)			

NOTES ....
....
....
....
....
....
....
....
....
....
....
....
....
....
....
....
....

Wedding Transportation And Planner Budget

Item	Budget	Spent	Paid
Bridal Party Transportation to the Ceremony Venue			
Bridal Party Transportation to the Reception Venue (if different from Ceremony Site)			
Gratuity for the Driver(s)			
Shuttle Service to transport guests to/from their hotels			
Valet Parking Service			
Day-Of, Month-Of or Full-Service Wedding Coordination			
Venue and/or Vendor Referrals and Liaison			
Budget Development			
Timeline Creation			
Rehearsal Coordination			
Wedding Day Setup and Management			

NOTES ....

....

....

....

....

....

....

....

....

....

....

....

....

....

....

Wedding Rings And Fund Budget

Item	Budget	Spent	Paid
Wedding Bands			
Wedding Band Resizing Fee			
Wedding Ring Insurance			
Any Customization / Engraving			
Vendor Tips			
Sales Tax			
Service Charges			
Wedding Insurance			
Liquor License (if not provided by the venue and/or caterer)			
Overtime Fees			

NOTES ....
....
....
....
....
....
....
....
....
....
....
....
....
....
....
....
....
....
....

Vendor Contact List

Baker

NAME: .... PHONE: ....

WEB: .... EMAIL: ....

ADDRESS: ....

Car/Shuttle

NAME: .... PHONE: ....

WEB: .... EMAIL: ....

ADDRESS: ....

Videographer

NAME: .... PHONE: ....

WEB: .... EMAIL: ....

ADDRESS: ....

Caterer

NAME: .... PHONE: ....

WEB: .... EMAIL: ....

ADDRESS: ....

Vendor Contact List

Liquor/ Bar Caterer

NAME: .... PHONE: ....

WEB: .... EMAIL: ....

ADDRESS: ....

Stationer

NAME: .... PHONE: ....

WEB: .... EMAIL: ....

ADDRESS: ....

Ceremony Venue

NAME: .... PHONE: ....

WEB: .... EMAIL: ....

ADDRESS: ....

Musicians/Deejay

NAME: .... PHONE: ....

WEB: .... EMAIL: ....

ADDRESS: ....

Vendor Contact List

Wedding Planner

NAME: ....   PHONE: ....

WEB: ....   EMAIL: ....

ADDRESS: ....

Dressmaker

NAME: ....   PHONE: ....

WEB: ....   EMAIL: ....

ADDRESS: ....

Officiant

NAME: ....   PHONE: ....

WEB: ....   EMAIL: ....

ADDRESS: ....

Florist

NAME: ....   PHONE: ....

WEB: ....   EMAIL: ....

ADDRESS: ....

Vendor Contact List

Seamstress Or Tailor

NAME: ....   PHONE: ....

WEB: ....   EMAIL: ....

ADDRESS: ....

Photographer

NAME: ....   PHONE: ....

WEB: ....   EMAIL: ....

ADDRESS: ....

Reception Venue

NAME: ....   PHONE: ....

WEB: ....   EMAIL: ....

ADDRESS: ....

Entertainment

NAME: ....   PHONE: ....

WEB: ....   EMAIL: ....

ADDRESS: ....

Wedding Table Layout

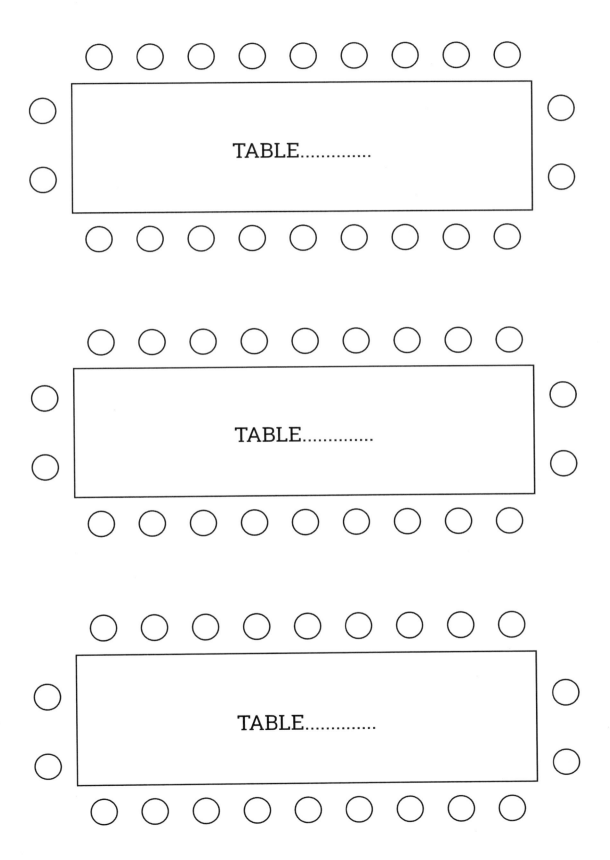

TABLE..............

TABLE..............

TABLE..............

Wedding Table Layout

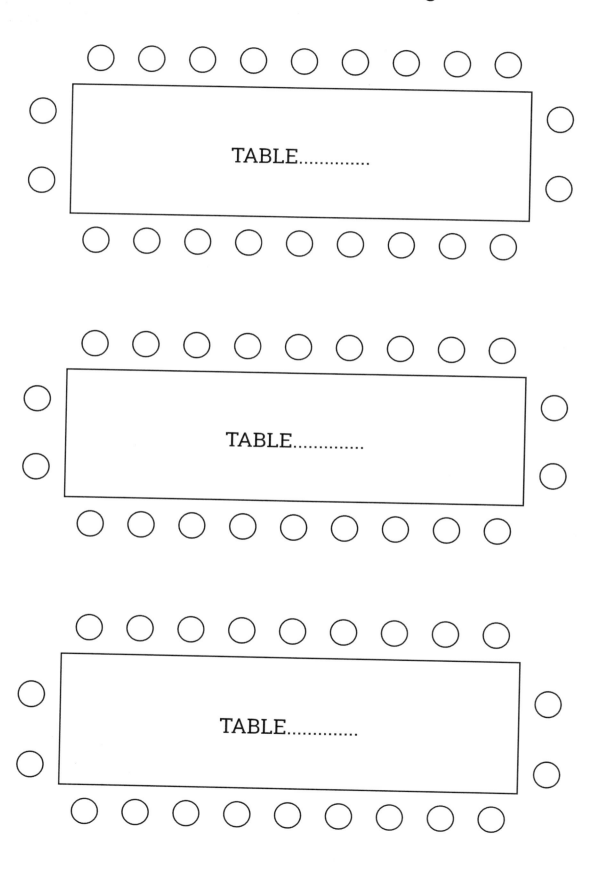

TABLE..............

TABLE..............

TABLE..............

Wedding Guest List

NO	GUEST'S NAME	COMPLETE ADDRESS	PHONE NUMBER	EMAIL ADDRESS
1				
2				
3				
4				
5				
6				
7				
8				
9				
10				
11				
12				
13				
14				
15				
16				
17				
18				
19				
20				
21				
22				
23				
24				
25				
26				
27				
28				
29				

Wedding Guest List

NO	GUEST'S NAME	COMPLETE ADDRESS	PHONE NUMBER	EMAIL ADDRESS
30				
31				
32				
33				
34				
35				
36				
37				
38				
39				
40				
41				
42				
43				
44				
45				
46				
47				
48				
49				
50				
51				
52				
53				
54				
55				
56				
57				
58				

Wedding Guest List

NO	GUEST'S NAME	COMPLETE ADDRESS	PHONE NUMBER	EMAIL ADDRESS
59				
60				
61				
62				
63				
64				
65				
66				
67				
68				
69				
70				
71				
72				
73				
74				
75				
76				
77				
78				
79				
80				
81				
82				
83				
84				
85				
86				
87				

Wedding Guest List

NO	GUEST'S NAME	COMPLETE ADDRESS	PHONE NUMBER	EMAIL ADDRESS
88				
89				
90				
91				
92				
93				
94				
95				
96				
97				
98				
99				
100				
101				
102				
103				
104				
105				
106				
107				
108				
109				
110				
111				
112				
113				
114				
115				
116				

Wedding Guest List

NO	GUEST'S NAME	COMPLETE ADDRESS	PHONE NUMBER	EMAIL ADDRESS
175				
176				
177				
178				
178				
179				
180				
181				
182				
183				
184				
185				
186				
187				
188				
189				
190				
191				
192				
193				
194				
195				
196				
197				
198				
199				
200				
201				
202				

Wedding Guest List

NO	GUEST'S NAME	COMPLETE ADDRESS	PHONE NUMBER	EMAIL ADDRESS
203				
204				
205				
206				
207				
208				
209				
210				
211				
212				
213				
214				
215				
216				
217				
218				
219				
220				
221				
221				
223				
224				
225				
226				
227				
228				
229				
230				
231				

Wedding Guest List

NO	GUEST'S NAME	COMPLETE ADDRESS	PHONE NUMBER	EMAIL ADDRESS
232				
233				
234				
235				
236				
237				
238				
239				
240				
241				
242				
243				
244				
245				
246				
247				
248				
249				
250				
251				
252				
253				
254				
255				
256				
257				
258				
259				
260				

To DO List

○ ....

○ ....

○ ....

○ ....

○ ....

○ ....

○ ....

○ ....

○ ....

○ ....

○ ....

○ ....

○ ....

○ ....

○ ....

○ ....

○ ....

○ ....

○ ....

○ ....

○ ....

○ ....

NOTES

IMPORTANT IDEAS

To DO List

- ○ ....
- ○ ....
- ○ ....
- ○ ....
- ○ ....
- ○ ....
- ○ ....
- ○ ....
- ○ ....
- ○ ....
- ○ ....
- ○ ....
- ○ ....
- ○ ....
- ○ ....
- ○ ....
- ○ ....
- ○ ....
- ○ ....
- ○ ....
- ○ ....
- ○ ....

NOTES

IMPORTANT IDEAS

To DO List

- ○ ....
- ○ ....
- ○ ....
- ○ ....
- ○ ....
- ○ ....
- ○ ....
- ○ ....
- ○ ....
- ○ ....
- ○ ....
- ○ ....
- ○ ....
- ○ ....
- ○ ....
- ○ ....
- ○ ....
- ○ ....
- ○ ....
- ○ ....
- ○ ....
- ○ ....
- ○ ....

NOTES

IMPORTANT IDEAS

To DO List

- ○ ....
- ○ ....
- ○ ....
- ○ ....
- ○ ....
- ○ ....
- ○ ....
- ○ ....
- ○ ....
- ○ ....
- ○ ....
- ○ ....
- ○ ....
- ○ ....
- ○ ....
- ○ ....
- ○ ....
- ○ ....
- ○ ....
- ○ ....
- ○ ....

NOTES

IMPORTANT IDEAS

To DO List

○ ....

○ ....

○ ....

○ ....

○ ....

○ ....

○ ....

○ ....

○ ....

○ ....

○ ....

○ ....

○ ....

○ ....

○ ....

○ ....

○ ....

○ ....

○ ....

○ ....

○ ....

○ ....

NOTES

IMPORTANT IDEAS

To DO List

- ○ ....
- ○ ....
- ○ ....
- ○ ....
- ○ ....
- ○ ....
- ○ ....
- ○ ....
- ○ ....
- ○ ....
- ○ ....
- ○ ....
- ○ ....
- ○ ....
- ○ ....
- ○ ....
- ○ ....
- ○ ....
- ○ ....
- ○ ....
- ○ ....

NOTES

IMPORTANT IDEAS

To DO List

O ....

O ....

O ....

O ....

O ....

O ....

O ....

O ....

O ....

O ....

O ....

O ....

O ....

O ....

O ....

O ....

O ....

O ....

O ....

O ....

O ....

NOTES

IMPORTANT IDEAS

To DO List

- ○ ....
- ○ ....
- ○ ....
- ○ ....
- ○ ....
- ○ ....
- ○ ....
- ○ ....
- ○ ....
- ○ ....
- ○ ....
- ○ ....
- ○ ....
- ○ ....
- ○ ....
- ○ ....
- ○ ....
- ○ ....
- ○ ....
- ○ ....

NOTES

IMPORTANT IDEAS

To DO List

○ ....

○ ....

○ ....

○ ....

○ ....

○ ....

○ ....

○ ....

○ ....

○ ....

○ ....

○ ....

○ ....

○ ....

○ ....

○ ....

○ ....

○ ....

○ ....

○ ....

NOTES

IMPORTANT IDEAS

To DO List

- ○ ....
- ○ ....
- ○ ....
- ○ ....
- ○ ....
- ○ ....
- ○ ....
- ○ ....
- ○ ....
- ○ ....
- ○ ....
- ○ ....
- ○ ....
- ○ ....
- ○ ....
- ○ ....
- ○ ....
- ○ ....
- ○ ....
- ○ ....
- ○ ....
- ○ ....

NOTES

IMPORTANT IDEAS

To DO List

O ....

O ....

O ....

O ....

O ....

O ....

O ....

O ....

O ....

O ....

O ....

O ....

O ....

O ....

O ....

O ....

O ....

O ....

O ....

O ....

O ....

O ....

NOTES

IMPORTANT IDEAS

To DO List

○ ....

○ ....

○ ....

○ ....

○ ....

○ ....

○ ....

○ ....

○ ....

○ ....

○ ....

○ ....

○ ....

○ ....

○ ....

○ ....

○ ....

○ ....

○ ....

○ ....

○ ....

NOTES

IMPORTANT IDEAS

To DO List

○ ....
○ ....
○ ....
○ ....
○ ....
○ ....
○ ....
○ ....
○ ....
○ ....
○ ....
○ ....
○ ....
○ ....
○ ....
○ ....
○ ....
○ ....
○ ....
○ ....
○ ....
○ ....

NOTES

IMPORTANT IDEAS

To DO List

○ ....

○ ....

○ ....

○ ....

○ ....

○ ....

○ ....

○ ....

○ ....

○ ....

○ ....

○ ....

○ ....

○ ....

○ ....

○ ....

○ ....

○ ....

○ ....

○ ....

○ ....

NOTES

IMPORTANT IDEAS

To DO List

- O ....
- O ....
- O ....
- O ....
- O ....
- O ....
- O ....
- O ....
- O ....
- O ....
- O ....
- O ....
- O ....
- O ....
- O ....
- O ....
- O ....
- O ....
- O ....
- O ....
- O ....
- O ....

NOTES

IMPORTANT IDEAS

To DO List

- O ....
- O ....
- O ....
- O ....
- O ....
- O ....
- O ....
- O ....
- O ....
- O ....
- O ....
- O ....
- O ....
- O ....
- O ....
- O ....
- O ....
- O ....
- O ....
- O ....
- O ....
- O ....

NOTES

IMPORTANT IDEAS

To DO List

○ ....
○ ....
○ ....
○ ....
○ ....
○ ....
○ ....
○ ....
○ ....
○ ....
○ ....
○ ....
○ ....
○ ....
○ ....
○ ....
○ ....
○ ....
○ ....
○ ....
○ ....
○ ....

NOTES

IMPORTANT IDEAS

To DO List

- ○ ....
- ○ ....
- ○ ....
- ○ ....
- ○ ....
- ○ ....
- ○ ....
- ○ ....
- ○ ....
- ○ ....
- ○ ....
- ○ ....
- ○ ....
- ○ ....
- ○ ....
- ○ ....
- ○ ....
- ○ ....
- ○ ....
- ○ ....
- ○ ....
- ○ ....

NOTES

IMPORTANT IDEAS

To DO List

- ○ ....
- ○ ....
- ○ ....
- ○ ....
- ○ ....
- ○ ....
- ○ ....
- ○ ....
- ○ ....
- ○ ....
- ○ ....
- ○ ....
- ○ ....
- ○ ....
- ○ ....
- ○ ....
- ○ ....
- ○ ....
- ○ ....
- ○ ....
- ○ ....
- ○ ....

NOTES

IMPORTANT IDEAS

To DO List

○ ....

○ ....

○ ....

○ ....

○ ....

○ ....

○ ....

○ ....

○ ....

○ ....

○ ....

○ ....

○ ....

○ ....

○ ....

○ ....

○ ....

○ ....

○ ....

○ ....

○ ....

NOTES

IMPORTANT IDEAS

To DO List

- ○ ....
- ○ ....
- ○ ....
- ○ ....
- ○ ....
- ○ ....
- ○ ....
- ○ ....
- ○ ....
- ○ ....
- ○ ....
- ○ ....
- ○ ....
- ○ ....
- ○ ....
- ○ ....
- ○ ....
- ○ ....
- ○ ....
- ○ ....
- ○ ....
- ○ ....
- ○ ....

NOTES

IMPORTANT IDEAS

To DO List

- ○ ....
- ○ ....
- ○ ....
- ○ ....
- ○ ....
- ○ ....
- ○ ....
- ○ ....
- ○ ....
- ○ ....
- ○ ....
- ○ ....
- ○ ....
- ○ ....
- ○ ....
- ○ ....
- ○ ....
- ○ ....
- ○ ....
- ○ ....
- ○ ....
- ○ ....

NOTES

IMPORTANT IDEAS

To DO List

○ ....

○ ....

○ ....

○ ....

○ ....

○ ....

○ ....

○ ....

○ ....

○ ....

○ ....

○ ....

○ ....

○ ....

○ ....

○ ....

○ ....

○ ....

○ ....

○ ....

NOTES

IMPORTANT IDEAS

To DO List

○ ....

○ ....

○ ....

○ ....

○ ....

○ ....

○ ....

○ ....

○ ....

○ ....

○ ....

○ ....

○ ....

○ ....

○ ....

○ ....

○ ....

○ ....

○ ....

○ ....

○ ....

NOTES

IMPORTANT IDEAS

To DO List

- ○ ....
- ○ ....
- ○ ....
- ○ ....
- ○ ....
- ○ ....
- ○ ....
- ○ ....
- ○ ....
- ○ ....
- ○ ....
- ○ ....
- ○ ....
- ○ ....
- ○ ....
- ○ ....
- ○ ....
- ○ ....
- ○ ....
- ○ ....
- ○ ....

NOTES

IMPORTANT IDEAS

To DO List

- ○ ....
- ○ ....
- ○ ....
- ○ ....
- ○ ....
- ○ ....
- ○ ....
- ○ ....
- ○ ....
- ○ ....
- ○ ....
- ○ ....
- ○ ....
- ○ ....
- ○ ....
- ○ ....
- ○ ....
- ○ ....
- ○ ....
- ○ ....
- ○ ....

NOTES

IMPORTANT IDEAS

To DO List

○ ....

○ ....

○ ....

○ ....

○ ....

○ ....

○ ....

○ ....

○ ....

○ ....

○ ....

○ ....

○ ....

○ ....

○ ....

○ ....

○ ....

○ ....

○ ....

○ ....

○ ....

NOTES

IMPORTANT IDEAS

To DO List

○ ....

○ ....

○ ....

○ ....

○ ....

○ ....

○ ....

○ ....

○ ....

○ ....

○ ....

○ ....

○ ....

○ ....

○ ....

○ ....

○ ....

○ ....

○ ....

○ ....

○ ....

NOTES

IMPORTANT IDEAS

To DO List

○ ....

○ ....

○ ....

○ ....

○ ....

○ ....

○ ....

○ ....

○ ....

○ ....

○ ....

○ ....

○ ....

○ ....

○ ....

○ ....

○ ....

○ ....

○ ....

○ ....

NOTES

IMPORTANT IDEAS

To DO List

- ○ ....
- ○ ....
- ○ ....
- ○ ....
- ○ ....
- ○ ....
- ○ ....
- ○ ....
- ○ ....
- ○ ....
- ○ ....
- ○ ....
- ○ ....
- ○ ....
- ○ ....
- ○ ....
- ○ ....
- ○ ....
- ○ ....
- ○ ....
- ○ ....

NOTES

IMPORTANT IDEAS

To DO List

○ ....
○ ....
○ ....
○ ....
○ ....
○ ....
○ ....
○ ....
○ ....
○ ....
○ ....
○ ....
○ ....
○ ....
○ ....
○ ....
○ ....
○ ....
○ ....
○ ....
○ ....

NOTES

IMPORTANT IDEAS

To DO List

○ ....
○ ....
○ ....
○ ....
○ ....
○ ....
○ ....
○ ....
○ ....
○ ....
○ ....
○ ....
○ ....
○ ....
○ ....
○ ....
○ ....
○ ....
○ ....
○ ....
○ ....

NOTES

IMPORTANT IDEAS

To DO List

○ ....

○ ....

○ ....

○ ....

○ ....

○ ....

○ ....

○ ....

○ ....

○ ....

○ ....

○ ....

○ ....

○ ....

○ ....

○ ....

○ ....

○ ....

○ ....

○ ....

NOTES

IMPORTANT IDEAS

To DO List

- ○ ....
- ○ ....
- ○ ....
- ○ ....
- ○ ....
- ○ ....
- ○ ....
- ○ ....
- ○ ....
- ○ ....
- ○ ....
- ○ ....
- ○ ....
- ○ ....
- ○ ....
- ○ ....
- ○ ....
- ○ ....
- ○ ....
- ○ ....

NOTES

IMPORTANT IDEAS

To DO List

- ○ ....
- ○ ....
- ○ ....
- ○ ....
- ○ ....
- ○ ....
- ○ ....
- ○ ....
- ○ ....
- ○ ....
- ○ ....
- ○ ....
- ○ ....
- ○ ....
- ○ ....
- ○ ....
- ○ ....
- ○ ....
- ○ ....
- ○ ....
- ○ ....
- ○ ....

NOTES

IMPORTANT IDEAS

To DO List

- ○ ....
- ○ ....
- ○ ....
- ○ ....
- ○ ....
- ○ ....
- ○ ....
- ○ ....
- ○ ....
- ○ ....
- ○ ....
- ○ ....
- ○ ....
- ○ ....
- ○ ....
- ○ ....
- ○ ....
- ○ ....
- ○ ....
- ○ ....
- ○ ....

NOTES

IMPORTANT IDEAS

To DO List

- O ....
- O ....
- O ....
- O ....
- O ....
- O ....
- O ....
- O ....
- O ....
- O ....
- O ....
- O ....
- O ....
- O ....
- O ....
- O ....
- O ....
- O ....
- O ....
- O ....
- O ....
- O ....

NOTES

IMPORTANT IDEAS

To DO List

- ○ ....
- ○ ....
- ○ ....
- ○ ....
- ○ ....
- ○ ....
- ○ ....
- ○ ....
- ○ ....
- ○ ....
- ○ ....
- ○ ....
- ○ ....
- ○ ....
- ○ ....
- ○ ....
- ○ ....
- ○ ....
- ○ ....
- ○ ....
- ○ ....

NOTES

IMPORTANT IDEAS

To DO List

- ○ ....
- ○ ....
- ○ ....
- ○ ....
- ○ ....
- ○ ....
- ○ ....
- ○ ....
- ○ ....
- ○ ....
- ○ ....
- ○ ....
- ○ ....
- ○ ....
- ○ ....
- ○ ....
- ○ ....
- ○ ....
- ○ ....
- ○ ....
- ○ ....

NOTES

IMPORTANT IDEAS

To DO List

○ ....

○ ....

○ ....

○ ....

○ ....

○ ....

○ ....

○ ....

○ ....

○ ....

○ ....

○ ....

○ ....

○ ....

○ ....

○ ....

○ ....

○ ....

○ ....

○ ....

NOTES

IMPORTANT IDEAS

To DO List

○ ....

○ ....

○ ....

○ ....

○ ....

○ ....

○ ....

○ ....

○ ....

○ ....

○ ....

○ ....

○ ....

○ ....

○ ....

○ ....

○ ....

○ ....

○ ....

○ ....

○ ....

○ ....

NOTES

IMPORTANT IDEAS

To DO List

- ○ ....
- ○ ....
- ○ ....
- ○ ....
- ○ ....
- ○ ....
- ○ ....
- ○ ....
- ○ ....
- ○ ....
- ○ ....
- ○ ....
- ○ ....
- ○ ....
- ○ ....
- ○ ....
- ○ ....
- ○ ....
- ○ ....
- ○ ....
- ○ ....
- ○ ....

NOTES

IMPORTANT IDEAS

To DO List

○ ....

○ ....

○ ....

○ ....

○ ....

○ ....

○ ....

○ ....

○ ....

○ ....

○ ....

○ ....

○ ....

○ ....

○ ....

○ ....

○ ....

○ ....

○ ....

○ ....

NOTES

IMPORTANT IDEAS

To DO List

- ○ ....
- ○ ....
- ○ ....
- ○ ....
- ○ ....
- ○ ....
- ○ ....
- ○ ....
- ○ ....
- ○ ....
- ○ ....
- ○ ....
- ○ ....
- ○ ....
- ○ ....
- ○ ....
- ○ ....
- ○ ....
- ○ ....
- ○ ....
- ○ ....
- ○ ....

NOTES

IMPORTANT IDEAS

To DO List

○ ....
○ ....
○ ....
○ ....
○ ....
○ ....
○ ....
○ ....
○ ....
○ ....
○ ....
○ ....
○ ....
○ ....
○ ....
○ ....
○ ....
○ ....
○ ....
○ ....
○ ....
○ ....

NOTES

IMPORTANT IDEAS

To DO List

- ○ ....
- ○ ....
- ○ ....
- ○ ....
- ○ ....
- ○ ....
- ○ ....
- ○ ....
- ○ ....
- ○ ....
- ○ ....
- ○ ....
- ○ ....
- ○ ....
- ○ ....
- ○ ....
- ○ ....
- ○ ....
- ○ ....
- ○ ....
- ○ ....

NOTES

IMPORTANT IDEAS

To DO List

○ ....

○ ....

○ ....

○ ....

○ ....

○ ....

○ ....

○ ....

○ ....

○ ....

○ ....

○ ....

○ ....

○ ....

○ ....

○ ....

○ ....

○ ....

○ ....

○ ....

○ ....

○ ....

NOTES

IMPORTANT IDEAS

To DO List

- O ....
- O ....
- O ....
- O ....
- O ....
- O ....
- O ....
- O ....
- O ....
- O ....
- O ....
- O ....
- O ....
- O ....
- O ....
- O ....
- O ....
- O ....
- O ....
- O ....
- O ....
- O ....
- O ....
- O ....

NOTES

IMPORTANT IDEAS

To DO List

○ ....

○ ....

○ ....

○ ....

○ ....

○ ....

○ ....

○ ....

○ ....

○ ....

○ ....

○ ....

○ ....

○ ....

○ ....

○ ....

○ ....

○ ....

○ ....

○ ....

NOTES

IMPORTANT IDEAS

To DO List

- ○ ....
- ○ ....
- ○ ....
- ○ ....
- ○ ....
- ○ ....
- ○ ....
- ○ ....
- ○ ....
- ○ ....
- ○ ....
- ○ ....
- ○ ....
- ○ ....
- ○ ....
- ○ ....
- ○ ....
- ○ ....
- ○ ....
- ○ ....
- ○ ....
- ○ ....

NOTES

IMPORTANT IDEAS

To DO List

○ ....

○ ....

○ ....

○ ....

○ ....

○ ....

○ ....

○ ....

○ ....

○ ....

○ ....

○ ....

○ ....

○ ....

○ ....

○ ....

○ ....

○ ....

○ ....

○ ....

○ ....

○ ....

NOTES

IMPORTANT IDEAS

To DO List

○ ....

○ ....

○ ....

○ ....

○ ....

○ ....

○ ....

○ ....

○ ....

○ ....

○ ....

○ ....

○ ....

○ ....

○ ....

○ ....

○ ....

○ ....

○ ....

○ ....

○ ....

NOTES

IMPORTANT IDEAS

To DO List

○ ....
○ ....
○ ....
○ ....
○ ....
○ ....
○ ....
○ ....
○ ....
○ ....
○ ....
○ ....
○ ....
○ ....
○ ....
○ ....
○ ....
○ ....
○ ....
○ ....
○ ....
○

NOTES

IMPORTANT IDEAS

To DO List

- ○ ....
- ○ ....
- ○ ....
- ○ ....
- ○ ....
- ○ ....
- ○ ....
- ○ ....
- ○ ....
- ○ ....
- ○ ....
- ○ ....
- ○ ....
- ○ ....
- ○ ....
- ○ ....
- ○ ....
- ○ ....
- ○ ....
- ○ ....
- ○ ....
- ○ ....

NOTES

IMPORTANT IDEAS

To DO List

○ ....
○ ....
○ ....
○ ....
○ ....
○ ....
○ ....
○ ....
○ ....
○ ....
○ ....
○ ....
○ ....
○ ....
○ ....
○ ....
○ ....
○ ....
○ ....
○ ....
○ ....

NOTES

IMPORTANT IDEAS

To DO List

○ ....

○ ....

○ ....

○ ....

○ ....

○ ....

○ ....

○ ....

○ ....

○ ....

○ ....

○ ....

○ ....

○ ....

○ ....

○ ....

○ ....

○ ....

○ ....

○ ....

○ ....

○ ....

NOTES

IMPORTANT IDEAS

To DO List

- ○ ....
- ○ ....
- ○ ....
- ○ ....
- ○ ....
- ○ ....
- ○ ....
- ○ ....
- ○ ....
- ○ ....
- ○ ....
- ○ ....
- ○ ....
- ○ ....
- ○ ....
- ○ ....
- ○ ....
- ○ ....
- ○ ....
- ○ ....

NOTES

IMPORTANT IDEAS

To DO List

○ ....

○ ....

○ ....

○ ....

○ ....

○ ....

○ ....

○ ....

○ ....

○ ....

○ ....

○ ....

○ ....

○ ....

○ ....

○ ....

○ ....

○ ....

○ ....

○ ....

○ ....

NOTES

IMPORTANT IDEAS

To DO List

○ ....

○ ....

○ ....

○ ....

○ ....

○ ....

○ ....

○ ....

○ ....

○ ....

○ ....

○ ....

○ ....

○ ....

○ ....

○ ....

○ ....

○ ....

○ ....

○ ....

○ ....

○ ....

NOTES

IMPORTANT IDEAS

To DO List

- ○ ....
- ○ ....
- ○ ....
- ○ ....
- ○ ....
- ○ ....
- ○ ....
- ○ ....
- ○ ....
- ○ ....
- ○ ....
- ○ ....
- ○ ....
- ○ ....
- ○ ....
- ○ ....
- ○ ....
- ○ ....
- ○ ....
- ○ ....
- ○ ....

NOTES

IMPORTANT IDEAS

To DO List

○ ....
○ ....
○ ....
○ ....
○ ....
○ ....
○ ....
○ ....
○ ....
○ ....
○ ....
○ ....
○ ....
○ ....
○ ....
○ ....
○ ....
○ ....
○ ....
○ ....

NOTES

IMPORTANT IDEAS

To DO List

○ ....
○ ....
○ ....
○ ....
○ ....
○ ....
○ ....
○ ....
○ ....
○ ....
○ ....
○ ....
○ ....
○ ....
○ ....
○ ....
○ ....
○ ....
○ ....
○ ....
○ ....
○ ....

NOTES

IMPORTANT IDEAS

To DO List

○ ....

○ ....

○ ....

○ ....

○ ....

○ ....

○ ....

○ ....

○ ....

○ ....

○ ....

○ ....

○ ....

○ ....

○ ....

○ ....

○ ....

○ ....

○ ....

○ ....

○ ....

○ ....

NOTES

IMPORTANT IDEAS

To DO List

○ ....

○ ....

○ ....

○ ....

○ ....

○ ....

○ ....

○ ....

○ ....

○ ....

○ ....

○ ....

○ ....

○ ....

○ ....

○ ....

○ ....

○ ....

○ ....

○ ....

○ ....

○ ....

NOTES

IMPORTANT IDEAS

To DO List

- ○ ....
- ○ ....
- ○ ....
- ○ ....
- ○ ....
- ○ ....
- ○ ....
- ○ ....
- ○ ....
- ○ ....
- ○ ....
- ○ ....
- ○ ....
- ○ ....
- ○ ....
- ○ ....
- ○ ....
- ○ ....
- ○ ....
- ○ ....
- ○ ....
- ○ ....
- ○ ....

NOTES

IMPORTANT IDEAS

To DO List

○ ....

○ ....

○ ....

○ ....

○ ....

○ ....

○ ....

○ ....

○ ....

○ ....

○ ....

○ ....

○ ....

○ ....

○ ....

○ ....

○ ....

○ ....

○ ....

○ ....

○ ....

NOTES

IMPORTANT IDEAS

To DO List

O ....

O ....

O ....

O ....

O ....

O ....

O ....

O ....

O ....

O ....

O ....

O ....

O ....

O ....

O ....

O ....

O ....

O ....

O ....

O ....

O ....

O ....

NOTES

IMPORTANT IDEAS

To DO List

- ○ ....
- ○ ....
- ○ ....
- ○ ....
- ○ ....
- ○ ....
- ○ ....
- ○ ....
- ○ ....
- ○ ....
- ○ ....
- ○ ....
- ○ ....
- ○ ....
- ○ ....
- ○ ....
- ○ ....
- ○ ....
- ○ ....
- ○ ....
- ○ ....

NOTES

IMPORTANT IDEAS

To DO List

○ ....

○ ....

○ ....

○ ....

○ ....

○ ....

○ ....

○ ....

○ ....

○ ....

○ ....

○ ....

○ ....

○ ....

○ ....

○ ....

○ ....

○ ....

○ ....

○ ....

○ ....

NOTES

IMPORTANT IDEAS

To DO List

- ○ ....
- ○ ....
- ○ ....
- ○ ....
- ○ ....
- ○ ....
- ○ ....
- ○ ....
- ○ ....
- ○ ....
- ○ ....
- ○ ....
- ○ ....
- ○ ....
- ○ ....
- ○ ....
- ○ ....
- ○ ....
- ○ ....
- ○ ....
- ○ ....

NOTES

IMPORTANT IDEAS

To DO List

○ ....
○ ....
○ ....
○ ....
○ ....
○ ....
○ ....
○ ....
○ ....
○ ....
○ ....
○ ....
○ ....
○ ....
○ ....
○ ....
○ ....
○ ....
○ ....
○ ....
○ ....
○ ....

NOTES

IMPORTANT IDEAS

To DO List

○ ....
○ ....
○ ....
○ ....
○ ....
○ ....
○ ....
○ ....
○ ....
○ ....
○ ....
○ ....
○ ....
○ ....
○ ....
○ ....
○ ....
○ ....
○ ....
○ ....

NOTES

IMPORTANT IDEAS

To DO List

○ ....
○ ....
○ ....
○ ....
○ ....
○ ....
○ ....
○ ....
○ ....
○ ....
○ ....
○ ....
○ ....
○ ....
○ ....
○ ....
○ ....
○ ....
○ ....
○ ....
○ ....

NOTES

IMPORTANT IDEAS

To DO List

- ○ ....
- ○ ....
- ○ ....
- ○ ....
- ○ ....
- ○ ....
- ○ ....
- ○ ....
- ○ ....
- ○ ....
- ○ ....
- ○ ....
- ○ ....
- ○ ....
- ○ ....
- ○ ....
- ○ ....
- ○ ....
- ○ ....
- ○ ....
- ○ ....
- ○ ....

NOTES

IMPORTANT IDEAS

To DO List

○ ....

○ ....

○ ....

○ ....

○ ....

○ ....

○ ....

○ ....

○ ....

○ ....

○ ....

○ ....

○ ....

○ ....

○ ....

○ ....

○ ....

○ ....

○ ....

○ ....

○ ....

NOTES

IMPORTANT IDEAS

To DO List

- ○ ....
- ○ ....
- ○ ....
- ○ ....
- ○ ....
- ○ ....
- ○ ....
- ○ ....
- ○ ....
- ○ ....
- ○ ....
- ○ ....
- ○ ....
- ○ ....
- ○ ....
- ○ ....
- ○ ....
- ○ ....
- ○ ....
- ○ ....
- ○ ....
- ○ ....

NOTES

IMPORTANT IDEAS

To DO List

- ○ ....
- ○ ....
- ○ ....
- ○ ....
- ○ ....
- ○ ....
- ○ ....
- ○ ....
- ○ ....
- ○ ....
- ○ ....
- ○ ....
- ○ ....
- ○ ....
- ○ ....
- ○ ....
- ○ ....
- ○ ....
- ○ ....
- ○ ....
- ○ ....

NOTES

IMPORTANT IDEAS

To DO List

- ○ ....
- ○ ....
- ○ ....
- ○ ....
- ○ ....
- ○ ....
- ○ ....
- ○ ....
- ○ ....
- ○ ....
- ○ ....
- ○ ....
- ○ ....
- ○ ....
- ○ ....
- ○ ....
- ○ ....
- ○ ....
- ○ ....
- ○ ....

NOTES

IMPORTANT IDEAS

To DO List

○ ....

○ ....

○ ....

○ ....

○ ....

○ ....

○ ....

○ ....

○ ....

○ ....

○ ....

○ ....

○ ....

○ ....

○ ....

○ ....

○ ....

○ ....

○ ....

○ ....

○ ....

○ ....

NOTES

IMPORTANT IDEAS

To DO List

- ○ ....
- ○ ....
- ○ ....
- ○ ....
- ○ ....
- ○ ....
- ○ ....
- ○ ....
- ○ ....
- ○ ....
- ○ ....
- ○ ....
- ○ ....
- ○ ....
- ○ ....
- ○ ....
- ○ ....
- ○ ....
- ○ ....
- ○ ....
- ○ ....
- ○ ....

NOTES

IMPORTANT IDEAS

To DO List

- ○ ....
- ○ ....
- ○ ....
- ○ ....
- ○ ....
- ○ ....
- ○ ....
- ○ ....
- ○ ....
- ○ ....
- ○ ....
- ○ ....
- ○ ....
- ○ ....
- ○ ....
- ○ ....
- ○ ....
- ○ ....
- ○ ....
- ○ ....
- ○ ....
- ○ ....
- ○ ....

NOTES

IMPORTANT IDEAS

To DO List

- ○ ....
- ○ ....
- ○ ....
- ○ ....
- ○ ....
- ○ ....
- ○ ....
- ○ ....
- ○ ....
- ○ ....
- ○ ....
- ○ ....
- ○ ....
- ○ ....
- ○ ....
- ○ ....
- ○ ....
- ○ ....
- ○ ....
- ○ ....
- ○ ....
- ○ ....

NOTES

IMPORTANT IDEAS

To DO List

○ ....
○ ....
○ ....
○ ....
○ ....
○ ....
○ ....
○ ....
○ ....
○ ....
○ ....
○ ....
○ ....
○ ....
○ ....
○ ....
○ ....
○ ....
○ ....
○ ....
○ ....

NOTES

IMPORTANT IDEAS

To DO List

- ○ ....
- ○ ....
- ○ ....
- ○ ....
- ○ ....
- ○ ....
- ○ ....
- ○ ....
- ○ ....
- ○ ....
- ○ ....
- ○ ....
- ○ ....
- ○ ....
- ○ ....
- ○ ....
- ○ ....
- ○ ....
- ○ ....
- ○ ....

NOTES

IMPORTANT IDEAS

To DO List

○ ....

○ ....

○ ....

○ ....

○ ....

○ ....

○ ....

○ ....

○ ....

○ ....

○ ....

○ ....

○ ....

○ ....

○ ....

○ ....

○ ....

○ ....

○ ....

○ ....

○ ....

NOTES

IMPORTANT IDEAS

To DO List

- ○ ....
- ○ ....
- ○ ....
- ○ ....
- ○ ....
- ○ ....
- ○ ....
- ○ ....
- ○ ....
- ○ ....
- ○ ....
- ○ ....
- ○ ....
- ○ ....
- ○ ....
- ○ ....
- ○ ....
- ○ ....
- ○ ....
- ○ ....
- ○ ....
- ○ ....

NOTES

IMPORTANT IDEAS

To DO List

- O ....
- O ....
- O ....
- O ....
- O ....
- O ....
- O ....
- O ....
- O ....
- O ....
- O ....
- O ....
- O ....
- O ....
- O ....
- O ....
- O ....
- O ....
- O ....
- O ....
- O ....
- O ....

NOTES

IMPORTANT IDEAS

To DO List

○ ....

○ ....

○ ....

○ ....

○ ....

○ ....

○ ....

○ ....

○ ....

○ ....

○ ....

○ ....

○ ....

○ ....

○ ....

○ ....

○ ....

○ ....

○ ....

○ ....

NOTES

IMPORTANT IDEAS

To DO List

○ ....

○ ....

○ ....

○ ....

○ ....

○ ....

○ ....

○ ....

○ ....

○ ....

○ ....

○ ....

○ ....

○ ....

○ ....

○ ....

○ ....

○ ....

○ ....

○ ....

○ ....

○ ....

NOTES

IMPORTANT IDEAS

To DO List

- ○ ....
- ○ ....
- ○ ....
- ○ ....
- ○ ....
- ○ ....
- ○ ....
- ○ ....
- ○ ....
- ○ ....
- ○ ....
- ○ ....
- ○ ....
- ○ ....
- ○ ....
- ○ ....
- ○ ....
- ○ ....
- ○ ....
- ○ ....

NOTES

IMPORTANT IDEAS

To DO List

○ ....

○ ....

○ ....

○ ....

○ ....

○ ....

○ ....

○ ....

○ ....

○ ....

○ ....

○ ....

○ ....

○ ....

○ ....

○ ....

○ ....

○ ....

○ ....

○ ....

○ ....

○ ....

NOTES

IMPORTANT IDEAS

Made in United States
North Haven, CT
11 May 2022

19112845R00067